ADVENTURE TIME

PRESENTS

MARCELINE

AND THE SCREAM QUEENS

ROSS RICHIE CEO & Founder • JACK CUMMINS President • MARK SMYLIE Chief Creative Officer • MATT GAGNON Editor-in-Chief • FILIP SABLIK VP of Publishing & Marketing • STEPHEN CHRISTY VP of Development
LANCE KREITER VP of Licensing & Merchandising • PHIL BARBARO VP of Finance • BRYCE CARLSON Managing Editor • MEL CAYLO Marketing Manager • SCOTT NEWMAN Production Design Manager • DAFNA PLEBAN Editor • SHANNON WATTERS Editor
ERIC HARBURN Editor • REBECCA TAYLOR Editor • CHRIS ROSA Assistant Editor • ALEX GALER Assistant Editor • WHITNEY LEOPARD Assistant Editor • JASMINE AMIRI Assistant Editor • MIKE LOPEZ Production Designer
HANNAH NANCE PARTLOW Production Designer • DEVIN FUNCHES E-Commerce & Inventory Coordinator • BRIANNA HART Executive Assistant • AARON FERRARA Operations Assistant • JOSE MEZA Sales Assistant

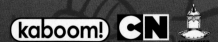

ADVENTURE TIME: MARCELINE AND THE SCREAM QUEENS Scholastic Edition, November 2013. Published by KaBOOM!, a division of Boom Entertainment, Inc. ADVENTURE TIME, CARTOON NETWORK, the logos, and all related characters and elements are trademarks of and © Cartoon Network. (S13) Originally published in single magazine form as ADVENTURE TIME: MARCELINE AND THE SCREAM QUEENS 1-6. © Cartoon Network. (S12) All rights reserved. KaBOOM!™ and the KaBOOM! logo are trademarks of Boom Entertainment, Inc., registered in various countries and categories. All characters, events, and institutions depicted herein are fictional. Any similarity between any of the names, characters, persons, events, and/or institutions in this publication to actual names, characters, and persons, whether living or dead, events, and/or institutions is unintended and purely coincidental. KaBOOM! does not read or accept unsolicited submissions of ideas, stories, or artwork.

For information regarding the CPSIA on this printed material, call: (203) 595-3636 and provide reference #RICH – 519528. A catalog record of this book is available from OCLC and from the KaBOOM! website, www.kaboom-studios.com, on the Librarians Page.

BOOM! Studios, 5670 Wilshire Boulevard, Suite 450, Los Angeles, CA 90036-5679. Printed in USA. First Printing.
ISBN: 978-1-60886-406-5, eISBN: 978-1-61398-260-0

"RESURRECTION SONG"
WRITTEN AND ILLUSTRATED BY
JEN WANG

"GRUMPY BUTT"
WRITTEN AND ILLUSTRATED BY
FAITH ERIN HICKS
COLORS BY MIRKA ANDOLFO

"FRUIT SALAD DAYS"
WRITTEN AND ILLUSTRATED BY
LIZ PRINCE

"THE BOOTLEGGER"
WRITTEN BY
YUKO OTA AND
ANANTH PANAGARIYA
ILLUSTRATED BY
YUKO OTA

"TREASURES UNTOLD"
WRITTEN AND ILLUSTRATED BY
KATE LETH

"COMMUNICATION ISSUES"
WRITTEN AND ILLUSTRATED BY
POLLY GUO

★ ★ ★ ADVENTURE TIME CREATED BY
PENDLETON WARD

★ ★ WRITTEN AND ILLUSTRATED BY
MEREDITH GRAN

★ ★ COLORS BY
LISA MOORE

★ ★ ★ LETTERS BY
STEVE WANDS

★ ★ COVER BY
JAB

EDITOR
SHANNON WATTERS
DESIGNER
KASSANDRA HELLER

WITH SPECIAL THANKS TO MARISA MARIONAKIS, RICK BLANCO, CURTIS LELASH, LAURIE HALAL-ONO, KEITH MACK, KELLY CREWS AND THE WONDERFUL FOLKS AT CARTOON NETWORK.

"THIS IS IT, YOU GUYS."

NEW SOUND.

NEW ALBUM.

NEW BOOTS!

OUR FIRST FULL-ON TOUR.

I'VE BEEN PSYCHING MYSELF UP FOR THIS FOR A **THOUSAND YEARS.**

WE'RE GONNA ROCK PEOPLE'S **BRAINS** OUT.

MEET SOME COOL LADIES...

LEARN TO WALK!

WE'LL BE DOING **SO MUCH** MORE THAN THAT, YOU GUYS.

OUR BAND'S GONNA CHANGE **LIVES.**

*FROM THE SCREAM QUEENS' HIT SINGLE, "BOYS FOR BREAKFAST"

OH YEAH, THESE DRUMSTICKS DATE BACK TO THE 3RD CENTURY AT THE **LATEST**.

100% STEGOSAURUS BONE. I TAKE REAL GOOD CARE OF 'EM.

YOUR AXE IS SUPER OLD TOO, AIN'T IT, MARCELINE?

DID WE SOUND OKAY OUT THERE TONIGHT? WAS IT JUST... BRAINLESS GOO...?

...

STOP WORRYING, MARCE. IT'S A **PARTY!**

YOU DIDN'T ANSWER ME!

JEEZ, MARCE. THIS IS JUST THE BEGINNING OF OUR TOUR...

YOU GONNA BE LIKE THIS THE **WHOLE** TIME?

MARCELINE!

HISSS!

OH, BONNIE! YOU MIGHT NOT WANNA GO IN--LET'S WALK **THIS** WAY!

I WANTED TO TELL YOU SOMETHING.

IS IT ABOUT MY STUPID BAND?

STUPID? **OH, NO WAY!**

I MEAN, WOW... I'VE ALWAYS LOOKED FOR SOME KIND OF **ORDER** IN MY MUSIC. STRUCTURE.

BUT WHAT YOU GUYS DO IS PURE PASSION... PURE ENERGY AND LOVE!

IT... IS?

YEAH.

I SHOULDN'T HAVE BEEN SO CRITICAL BEFORE.

Thank you for unleashing me from my curse! I've been trapped in the guitar for months but no one would play me because they think I'm a monster.

You're not a genie at all! YOU LIED TO ME!!

I warned you

what would happen

if you lied to me...

Oh Anbaris! You're alive!

It'd been so long, I thought I'd lost you forever!

Thanks, Monster Lady!

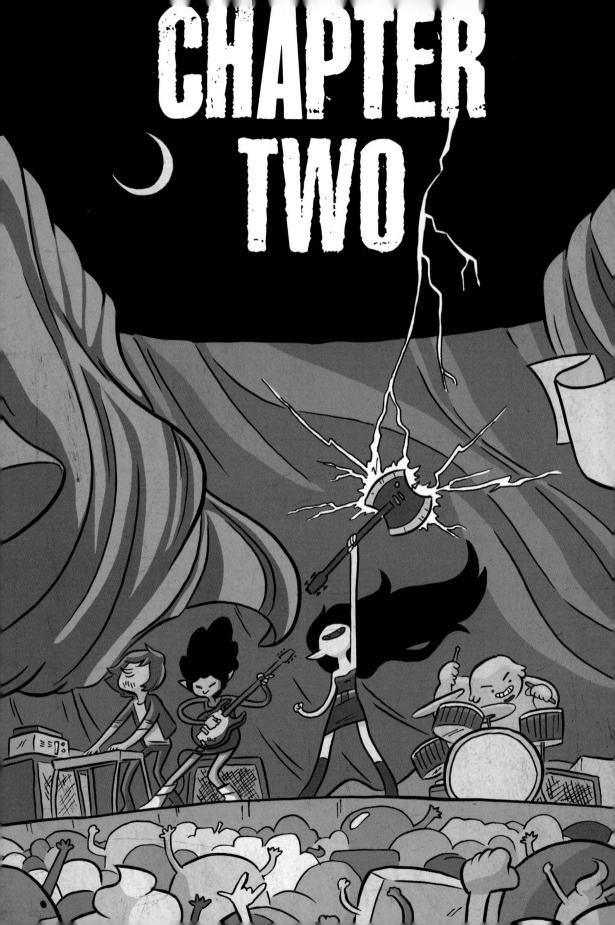

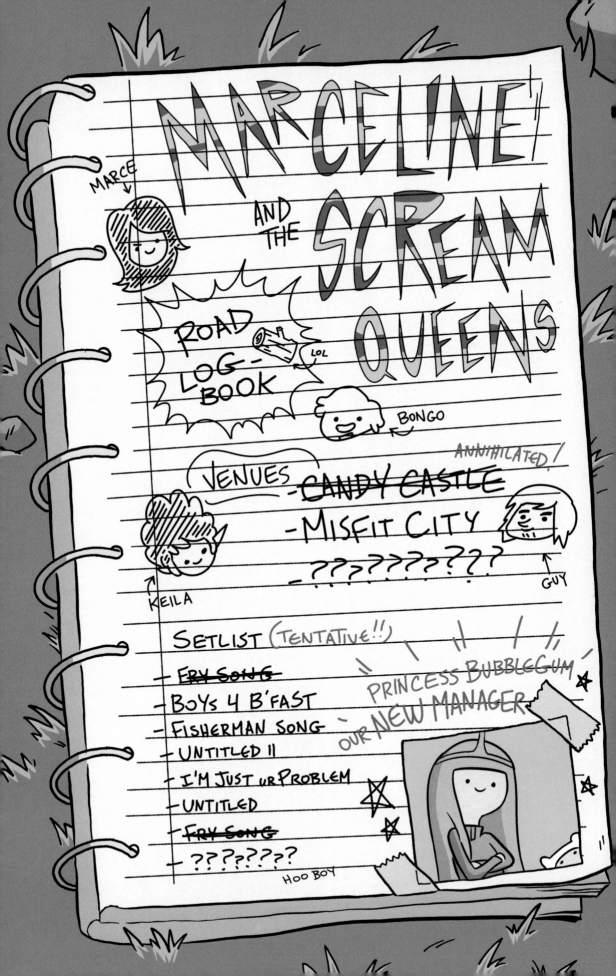

HISSS!

ARE YOU GHOULS **CRAZY?** THIS PLACE LOOKS LIKE BARF KINGDOM--MINUS ALL THE **MAJESTY!**

MAN, THAT'S RIGHT...MARCE AND KEILA WERE ON A RED BENDER LAST NIGHT.

I THOUGHT WE ALL **AGREED** TO GO TO BED **ON TIME.**

BUT, PRINCESS! IT WAS **LEGENDARY!**

AN ENTIRE FOREST OF APPLES AND BERRIES... **DE-PIGMENTED!**

I CAN STILL **TASTE** 'EM.

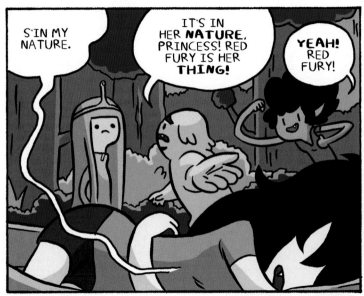

S'IN MY NATURE.

IT'S IN HER **NATURE**, PRINCESS! RED FURY IS HER **THING**!

YEAH! RED FURY!

RED FURY!

RED FURY!

RED FURY!

NUTS TO THAT! I SIGNED UP TO BE YOUR MANAGER-- NOT YOUR **MOM**.

ARE A BUNCH OF SELF-MADE MUSICIANS REALLY THIS **HELPLESS**?

IT'S NOT VERY "**PUNK ROCK**" OF YOU.

WHAT?!

THE FARTHEST CORNER OF MY *BUTT* IS MORE PUNK ROCK THAN YOU!

GUYS...

WE'D BETTER GET READY FOR THAT INTERVIEW...IT'S IN HALF AN HOUR.

OH, WADS!!

I JUST NEED TO SET MY RECORDER, AND WE CAN GET STARTED...

CAN I JUST SAY WHAT AN **HONOR** IT IS TO BE INTERVIEWED?

AH, WELL, Y'KNOW... MY COLLEGE GIVES **CREDIT** FOR THIS KINDA THING, SO...

PECK PECK PECK PECK PECK

HM.

PECK PECK PECK PECK PECK PECK PECK PECK PECK PECK PECK PECK PECK...

SO ARE THE **BEAN QUEENS** CURRENTLY LOOKING FOR A RECORD LABEL?

THE **WHO?!**

T-THE **SCREAM** QUEENS...

EH, YEAH... WE'D BE OPEN, I GUESS. TO THE RIGHT LABEL...

THAT WAS **INSULTING**. WAS SHE EVEN A REAL **SQUIRREL?**

LET'S HEAD DOWN TO THE VENUE. THEY WANT TO DO A PRE-SHOW RADIO SEGMENT.

FORGET IT. **NO MORE** INTERVIEWS!

LET'S TALK **LUNCH.** WHAT'VE WE GOT, BAND MANAGER?

WHAT?

SINCE WHEN IS LUNCH **MY** JOB?

SINCE I GOT **MAD HUNGRY.**

THERE'S GOTTA BE SOME **RED** AROUND HERE SOMEWH--

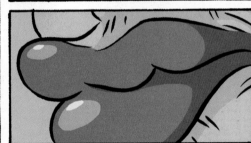

OH MY **GLOB...**

SCREAM QUEENS, EH? HEARD OF YOU.

LORD VANDALSTINE!

PRINCESS BUBBLEGUM, BAND MANAGER.

GUTEN TAG, PRINCESS. CALL ME **SLICKO**.

SEHR ERFREUT.

TELL ME, WHAT BRINGS YOU TO **MISFIT CITY?**

WELL... THIS PLACE IS A HOTBED FOR **PUNK INNOVATION.** MANY OF THE BAND'S INFLUENCES STARTED HERE.

SO **NATURALLY** WE'D TOUR HERE.

YES, OF **COURSE!**

WOULD YOU ALL LIKE TO GET LUNCH? I'M GOING TO MY **FAVE** SPOT AND I'D LOVE TO TALK.

GEEZ... WELL, WE NEED TO SET UP FOR THE SHOW...

BUT **MARCELINE** CAN GO!

WHA...?

THAT'S RIGHT--I MADE LUNCH PLANS FOR YOU AFTER ALL!

HAVE FUN!

SPLENDID!

WOW, HE'S HEARD OF US!

DUDE!

MAN, I'VE GOT THE CBGBs...

THAT WAS REALLY **SMOOTH** OF YOU, PRINCESS.

JUST CALL ME BUBBLEGUM.

BUBBLEGUM. YOU'RE REALLY DOIN' **A LOT** FOR THIS BAND.

YOU THINK SO?

FOR **SURE!** AND IT MEANS A LOT TO US.

I KNOW WE'VE ONLY MET RECENTLY, BUT... I FEEL LIKE I CAN **TRUST** YOU.

AW MAN... IS THAT **WEIRD?!**

HA HA, NO! THAT'S VERY SWEET OF YOU, GUY.

COOL. SO WHERE THE HECK DID YOU LEARN **GERMAN?**

I'M SURPRISED TO HEAR YOU'RE LOOKING FOR A **LABEL**, MARCELINE.

AREN'T YOU MORE OF THE D.I.Y. TYPE?

A NO-FRILLS, UNAPOLOGETIC, STAGE DIVING **PUNK-ROCKER?**

WELL SURE, THAT'S ME...

BUT I KNOW WHERE I **COME FROM,** MAN, AND A LABEL HAS **BEANS** TO DO WITH THAT.

I'M HAPPY TO HEAR THAT. WE STRIVE TO WORK WITH OUR ARTISTS' **UNIQUE** PERSONALITIES.

VANDALOUS RECORDS IS A FACE-MELTINGLY **HIP** LABEL.

WE WANT TO ENABLE OUR TALENT TO BE THEMSELVES AT ALL TIMES.

...TO EXPRESS ALL OF THEIR **NEEDS** TO US...

ALL OF THEIR DESIRES.

DON'T YOU AGREE?

CAN I HAVE A HUGE BITE OF THAT??

YOU'RE AN ECCENTRIC, ALL RIGHT. **I LOVE IT!**

EH HEH

WELL, THE SOUND IS **GARBAGE**... SO WE'RE **READY!**

ARE YOU IN HERE, GUY? THE BAND'S ON IN TWENTY.

GUY...?

BUBBLEGUM...

I-I DIDN'T WANT YOU TO **FIND OUT** THIS WAY...

OH MY GOSH. YOU'RE A **WEREWOLF?**

YES.

IT'S MY VERY SEXY CURSE. HOW CAN I GO **OUT THERE** LIKE THIS?

I UNDERSTAND IF YOU **HATE** ME...

C'MON, I DON'T MIND...

THAT'S ACTUALLY KINDA **COOL**.

Grumpy Butt

by

FAITH

ERIN

HICKS

LOOK MARCELINE! OUR MUSICAL JOURNEY THROUGH THE LAND OF *OOO* HAS BROUGHT US TO THE SMALL HAMLET OF *BLOOO*, A REGION FAMOUS FOR ... WELL, BEING BLUE!

UGH. THIS PLACE IS WAYYY TOO MONOCHROMATIC.

I THINK IT'S *LOVELY* HOW EVERYTHING MATCHES.

LOOK, BLUE TREES!

UGH.

BLUE ROCKS!

UGH!

OVER THERE! TINY BLUE INTERPRETATIONAL DANCERS!

UGH! THEY'RE THE WORST OF ALL.

WELL! SOMEONE HAS *HER* GRUMPY BUTT ON.

WHATEVS. I'M GONNA GO EAT SOMETHING.

HM.

← BLUE!

HUH.

BLUE! →

BLUE! ↓

ARGH.

B.G.

MAP OF Ooo

HAVE YOU NOTICED THE COMPLETE LACK OF RED IN THIS SMALL HAMLET OF BLOOO? AND, Y'KNOW, I KIND OF *EAT* RED.

SO, JUST SAYING, WE PROBABLY SHOULD'VE PLANNED FOR THIS ...

'CAUSE I'M STARVING!

OH.

OH, I DID PLAN FOR THIS. I BROUGHT KEVIN!

IS KEVIN RED? CAN I EAT HIM?

NO, NO, KEVIN IS A ROBOT! I MADE HIM IN MY SPARE TIME, WHEN I WASN'T TENDING TO MY PRINCESS DUTIES.

HEH, *DUTIES.*

WHAT?

NOTHIN'.

HERE HE IS!

'ELLO MUM! I'VE COME TO DO YOUR BIDDING!

PIP PIP!

CHEERIO OLD BEAN!

UH HUUHH.

HUP! HUP!

KEVIN'S JOB IS TO PAINT THINGS RED.

HUP! HUP!

GOOD JOB!

SO WHILE YOU'RE OFF PLAYING TODAY'S CONCERT, HE'LL PAINT YOU UP A DELICIOUS BATCH OF RED!

AND HIS NAME IS KEVIN?

YEP!

COOL.

LATER--

GOOD EVENING RESIDENTS OF BLOOO! WE ARE THE SCREAM QUEENS AND I HOPE YOU ENJOY OUR MUSICAL STYLIZATIONS!

FOR A BUNCH OF BLUE DUDES, THE BLOOOBIANS WERE PRETTY GOOD AT ROCKING OUT.

YES, QUITE GOOD.

KEVIN!!

LOOK WHAT KEVIN DID!

NO, KEVIN, THAT'S *WRONG!*

I MADE YOU TO PAINT THINGS *RED*, NOT PAINT GIANT MURALS USING EVERY COLOR *BUT* RED!

KEVIN DID WRONG?

HUN. GRY.

YES! KEVIN DID *VERY* WRONG!

BUT ... BUT THE *MUSIC!* IT MADE KEVIN FEEL FEELINGS THAT WEREN'T RED! KEVIN WANTED TO PAINT THE COLORS THE MUSIC MADE HIM *FEEL*.

OH KEVIN, I THINK I UNDERSTAND.

YOU HEARD MARCELINE PLAYING HER MUSIC AND WANTED TO EXPRESS YOURSELF.

YES, KEVIN PAINTED THE COLORS.

AND THEY'RE BEAUTIFUL, BUT KEVIN, YOU NEEDED TO DO YOUR JOB FIRST.

I AM PRINCESS BUBBLEGUM, RULER OF THE CANDY KINGDOM.

I'M ALSO A BAND MANAGER--

-- AND A SCIENTIST (WHO MADE YOU).

I LOVE BEING A SCIENTIST AND MANAGING A ROCK BAND, BUT I WOULD NEVER LET MUSIC OR SCIENCE DISTRACT ME FROM MY PRINCESS DUTIES.

BECAUSE BEING A PRINCESS AND RULING THE CANDY KINGDOM IS MY JOB!

KIND OF HUNGRY YOU GUYS!

RAAHHH

LET'S PAINT UP SOME RED TO FIX MARCELINE'S GRUMPY BUTT, AND THEN YOU CAN FINISH YOUR NOT-RED PAINTING.

THE END!

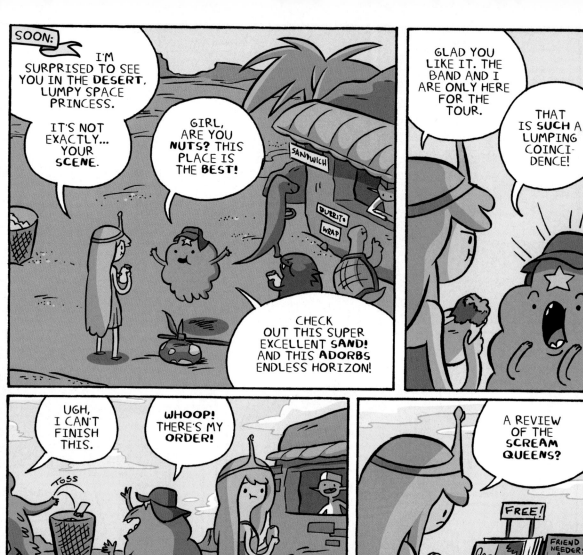

"FORGETTABLE MELODIES..."

"...TRITE LYRICIST..."

SCRIBBA
SCRIBBA
SCRIBBA

I'LL GIVE THEM **TRITE!**

WAIT. WHAT'S TRITE MEAN?

OUCH.

THAT'S WHEN SOMETHING'S, LIKE, **LUKEWARM.**

I THOUGHT IT MEANT "BUTT-SHAPED".

THEY WANT **LUKEWARM,** HUH? THEY WANT **BUTT-SHAPED?!**

H-HEY... CAN I GET YOUR AUTO-GRAPH?

GO FLIP A SQUID. —M

WELL... THAT WAS JUST A COVER-UP.

TO HIDE THE **REAL** TRUTH...

...THAT I'M ACTUALLY A **WERE-FISH**.

WHOA!

WAIT, HOW DOES THAT WORK?

I CAN BREATHE UNDERWATER. AND SOMETIMES I GET THESE CRAZY URGES...TO EAT KELP.

OH.

I'M A MONSTER! I NEVER ASKED TO BE SO HORRIBLE.

GUY! YOU CAN'T DOUBT YOURSELF! THAT'S WHAT MARCELINE DOES!

IT'S A TOXIC WASTE OF YOUR TIME!

I KNOW!

AND I MEAN... I **LIKE** FISH. FISH ARE TOTALLY OKAY.

YOU'RE TOTALLY OKAY.

GUY, GET OUT HERE. WE'RE COORDINATING STAGE OUTFITS.

OH, RIGHT!

WE WERE JUST PRACTICING--

FOR THE SMOOCH OLYMPICS??

HURRY UP.

TO BE CONTINUED?

REMEMBER TO CHECK THE COLORS ON YOUR MIXER.

SLAM!

WERE-FISH.

FRUIT SALAD DAYS   by LIZ PRINCE 2012

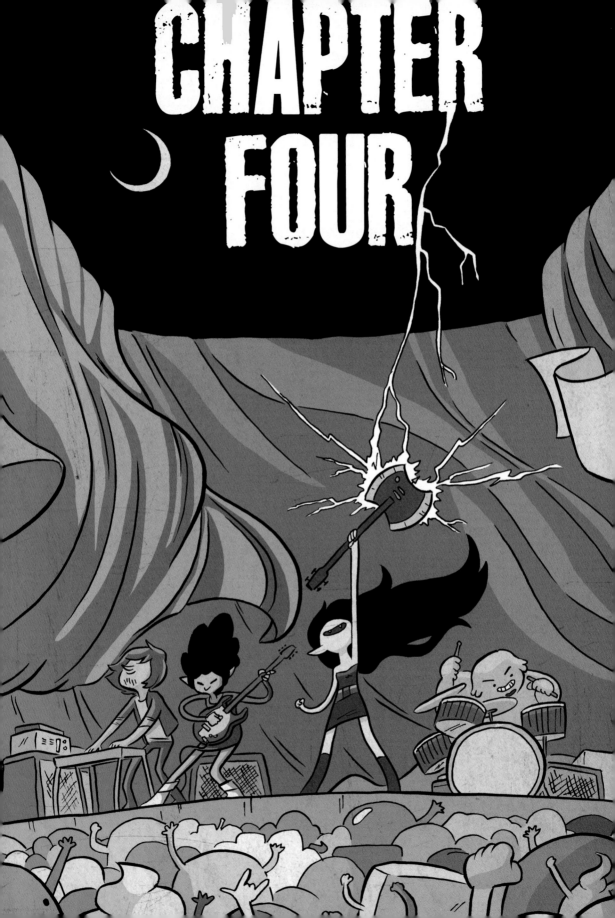

O.M.....G!!
WEEKLY

Qoo Presents

Marceline & The Scream Queens are totally...

OUTTA CONTROL!!!

Marce REFUSING to look at her fans for even like half a second??

Keila's TEARFUL CONFESSION: "A psychic wrote my songs."

2 DAYS. SAME HOODIE.

Princess "Trouble"gum has "HAD IT", says source

PLUS: Mysterious keyboardist Guy is a were-fish HAS A GIRLFRIEND?!?

Band looking to replace Bongo after he "goes country"

Biggest Scandal of my *LIFE!!*

UH.

W-WHAT WAS I JUST SINGING?

FISHER-MAN SONG!

THE MIGHTY TIDE!

WHAT THE HECK SONG IS **THAT?**

WELL, JUST YESTERDAY:

IS EVERYONE'S PRESSURE ELIXIR WORKING?

NOBODY DEAD?

I'M DEAD.

I'M UNDEAD.

OKAY OKAY, SHUT UP.

HOW ABOUT YOU, MARCELINE?

...

MINE WORKS GREAT.

YOU'RE A GENIUS.

THIS WAY, GUESTS!

SOUND CITY IS NAMED FOR THE BODY OF WATER -- NOT OUR APPRECIATION FOR THE AURAL ARTS.

THOUGH WE HAVE PLENTY OF THAT.

CAN YOU EVEN HEAR MUSIC DOWN HERE?

YOU'RE ESPECIALLY LUCKY TO BE HERE DURING THE CALM, WHEN SOUND CITY IS AT ITS MOST BEAUTIFUL!

THE CALM?

THE SCREAM QUEENS! WELCOME!

OCEAN PRINCESS. THANK YOU FOR ACCOMMODATING US **SO** GENEROUSLY!

YEAH, WE USUALLY SLEEP IN FILTH.

THE PLEASURE IS MINE! MY PEOPLE ARE **ENTHUSIASTIC** PATRONS OF "ROCK MUSIC."

WITH ITS MULTIPLE NOTES AND ITS CRISP YET DEEP RESONANCE!

YOUR PEOPLE HAVE SUCH A QUIET ELEGANCE.

JUST ENJOYING LIFE!

YES, TRANQUILITY IS LAW.

IS THAT WHAT YOUR CHAPERONE MEANT, THEN? BY "THE CALM"?

NO... THAT IS SOMETHING ELSE.

OUR WORLD CAN OCCASIONALLY FALL INTO CHAOS, AND WE MUST FLOW ALONG WITH IT.

AS A PRINCESS OF YOUR OWN KINGDOM, SURELY YOU UNDERSTAND THAT.

OF...OF COURSE.

SPEAKING OF WHICH, OUR ANTENNA TOWERS CAN BE USED TO COMMUNICATE ABOVE-GROUND, IF YOU'D LIKE.

THERE'S A STATION NEAR YOUR GUEST QUARTERS.

OH, GREAT!

P.B.! IS THAT YOU?

FINN! IT'S SO GOOD TO HEAR YOUR VOICE.

YEAH! I BET YOU MISS THE CANDY KINGDOM, HUH?

OH, Y'KNOW... A LITTLE...

WELL DON'T WORRY, 'CAUSE JAKE'S BEEN HOLDIN' IT DOWN HARDCORE.

LIKE YESTERDAY, WE HAD THIS SCREAM-OFF TO COMMEMORATE THE NEW FUNGEON?

FUNGEON?

OH, YEAH. WHERE THE DUNGEON USED TO BE.

TOTES WHAT IT SOUNDS LIKE.

USED TO--??!

W-WHERE ARE THE PRISONERS?

HANG ON PEEBS, I CAN'T REALLY HEAR YOU WITH THE **RULE BURNING CEREMONY** GOING ON...

YOU NOCTURNAL NIMROD! ARE YOU TRYING TO MAKE **EVERYONE** MISERABLE?

...HEY, WHAT A GOOD IDEA.

I'M **SICK** OF THIS ATTITUDE. **WHY** ARE YOU **BEING** LIKE THIS??

YOU'RE STILL READING THOSE...?

I TOLD YOU **NOT** TO--

DON'T **LECTURE** ME.

HOW AM I SUPPOSED TO RESIST?!

IT'S LIKE CANDY THAT **HATES YOU!**

HMPH...SOUNDS EASY ENOUGH TO ME.

YOU DON'T UNDERSTAND. HOW **CAN** YOU?

YOU'RE A PRINCESS WITH A KINGDOM. YOU'RE IN **CONTROL** OF YOUR WORLD.

I'M NOT *ALWAYS* IN CONTROL.

FLOW
WITH
IT.

OH, I--

THAT WAS THE **MOST** CONCERT WE'VE EVER **HAD**!

OH MY GLOB, I HEARD LIKE 3 NOTES!

IT WAS **DEFINITELY** MUSIC.

FANTASTIC! WHAT A SHOW!

ARE YOU TWO ALL RIGHT?

YEAH MAN. THAT WASN'T BAD AT ALL! IT WAS KIND OF A RUSH.

YES! THE DAY'S WORRIES ARE OFFICIALLY OVER.

DOES THE TIDE COME IN LIKE THAT...**EVERY** DAY??

OH YES...EVERY 24 HOURS, ON THE NOSE!

DUDE...LET'S GET OUT OF HERE.

SERIOUSLY.

TO BE CONTINUED NEXT CHAPTER!

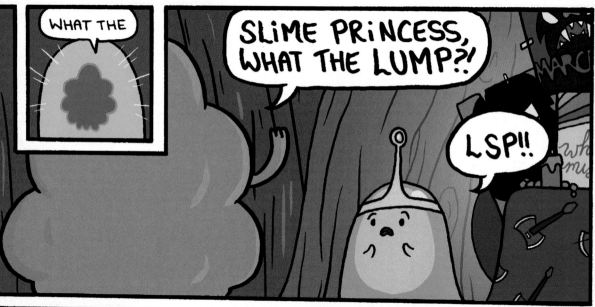

THIS IS MY STUFF!

THIS IS MY MARCELINE AT THE UNDERGROUND SPECIAL RECORD!

AND THESE ARE MY BUBBLEGUM BANGLES!

AND THIS IS MY FAVORITE THING *ever*!!!

THIS SHIRT IS LIKE **SO** RARE!

YOU CAN TRY IT ON IF YOU WANT, I GUESS

SHUFF
SHUFF
SHUFF

OH MY GLOB GIRL

YOU LOOK AWESOME!

END!

Whaaaat? Starchy bought that ticket fair and square!

Where did you get it?

From a fella in an alley!

If Starchy can't see the show, Starchy wants a refund!

Cinnamon Bun ... give Starchy his *refund.*

heh heh

It looks like we have some work to do!

M-MAYBE WE SHOULD TELL THE P-PRINCESS AN' MARCELINE ...

No, we mustn't trouble the Princess.

It is a butler's sacred duty to take care of these problems...

BY ANY MEANS NECESSARY.

They're all up there, being all *YOUNG* and *BEAUTIFUL* and *HIP* and *YOUNG* ...

... no room for ol' Ice King, oh no ...

I can play the drums! I'm really good at them.

I've been practicing! Wanna hear?

Cinammon Bun ... Show him what we do to DRUMS ...

WHEEEEEEEE

MY DRUM KIT! Who's going to pay for that? I want a refund!

That ...

... can be arranged.

the end

CHAPTER FIVE

THIS IS JUST DELIGHTFUL! YOU BROUGHT THE WHOLE GANG.

I CAN FINALLY SEE WHAT MY LITTLE GIRL **DOES!**

I'VE **TOLD** YOU WHAT I DO, DADDY.

YOU REALLY **DON'T** NEED TO COME TONIGHT.

OH, DON'T WORRY. I'LL STAND IN THE BACK. YOU WON'T EVEN SEE ME ROCKIN' UP!

ROCKIN' AROUND! HA HA!

YEAH, MR. ABADEER!

WHIIIIIDDLIDLIDLE! MANANANANAAAAAAAA BDA-BDA BM-CHSH! BOOM!

AUGH! DAD ROCK!!

AND **YOU!**

YOU MUST BE PRINCESS BUBBLEGUM! I'VE HEARD SO MUCH ABOUT YOU!

W-WE REALLY GOTTA GO, DAD!

NO TIME FOR PIE! SET-UP TIME!

WHAT? NO! EVEN I DISAGREE WITH THAT!

WHAT A **NIGHTMARE**.

CAN'T I RELAX WHILE VISITING HOME...JUST ONCE?

I LIKE YOUR DAD! HE'S A DUDE WHO TAKES WHAT HE WANTS.

WELL, WELL. LOOK WHO CAME SLITHERING BACK.

YEAH. WHAT HE WANTS.

TUFF!

YOU STILL WORK HERE!

YEAH, MAN. I'VE BEEN SETTIN' UP YOUR GEAR FOR TONIGHT!

AND I'VE GOT A SPECIAL REQUEST... IF YOU'RE **UP** TO IT!

WE WERE KINDA HOPING FOR AN ACOUSTIC SET TONIGHT!

OOOH.

NICE PIANO!

YEAH. I REMEMBER YOU.

WHAT THE HECK ARE **THESE?**

WELL, I'VE BEEN GONE SO LONG, THINGS CAN GET A LITTLE BLURRED... THERE'S NO SUMMING UP MY THOUGHTS OR MY EXPERIENCE WITH WORDS...

ONLY SOUNDS AND SMELL AND TEXTURE,
SO FAMILIAR AND KIND,
SMALL MEMORIES THAT RECONNECT THE
DOTS IN SPACES OF MY MIND...

I'M SO VERY PROUD TO BE HERE,
WITH MY MONSTER PALS AROUND
TO END MY SEARCH AT THE BEGINNING,
FOR WHAT I ALREADY HAD FOUND.

THERE SHE IS!

MY LITTLE ROCK DEVO!

THANKS FOR COMING, EVERYONE.

WASN'T SHE MAGNIFICENT?

I'LL SAY.

I KNEW YOU COULD PULL IT OFF! WE ALL DID.

THOSE BAD REVIEWS WERE A BUNCH O' BA-**NAY-NAYS!**

WAIT...

YOU HAVE THOSE HORRIBLE **GOSSIP MAGAZINES** DOWN HERE?!

YEAH!

HORRIBLE GOSSIP MAGS ARE **ALL** WE HAVE IN THE NIGHTOSPHERE!

HA HA HA HA HA HA HAHAHA! HAHA HA HA HA HA HA!

GLOB, THIS WHOLE TOUR'S BEEN A DISASTER.

WHAT ARE YOU **TALKING** ABOUT??!

EVERY TOWN WE VISIT **LOVES** YOU!

LOVES ME?! ARE YOU **BLIND?**

THE ENTIRE WORLD **HATES** ME!

HATES ME. HATES ME HATES ME HATES ME

HATES ME.

IT'S OVER, BONNIE. THIS BAND WAS SUPPOSED TO DO AMAZING THINGS.

IT WAS SUPPOSED TO CHANGE **LIVES**.

IT CHANGED MINE.

NOT THAT IT MATTERS.

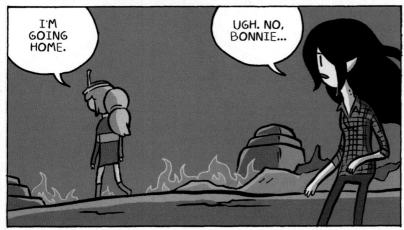

I'M GOING HOME.

UGH. NO, BONNIE...

THE TRUTH IS...I'M JUST A **GUY**.

A GUY

WHO CAN SHIFT

INTO ANY FORM.

THAT MEANS...

IT MEANS YOU HAVE INFINITE POTENTIAL!

WHY WOULD YOU MAKE UP SOME PHONY IDENTITY?

EVERYBODY **ELSE** IS SOMETHING COOL! I WANTED PEOPLE TO **LIKE** ME!

...I WANTED **YOU** TO LIKE ME.

MY SPECIES HAS BEEN UNDER-ACHIEVING FOR CENTURIES. AND OUR LIVES ARE SO LONG.

I'VE BEEN PUTTING OFF FINDING MYSELF FOR A LONG TIME.

GUY...

SHOW ME YOUR TRUE FORM.

...I DON'T EVEN REMEMBER IT.

I MODELED THIS ONE AFTER MY HEROES...THE ROCK STARS OF LEGEND.

THAT'S ALL I EVER WANTED TO BE.

DUDE...WHAT IF I STAYED HERE? GOT BACK INTO THE LOCAL SCENE. WOULD THAT BE CRAZY?!

HA HA... I DUNNO IF IT WOULD BE CRAZY!

BUT, Y'KNOW...NOT MUCH HAPPENS IN THIS TOWN. NO ONE WHO STAYS HERE BECOMES A STAR.

YEAH.

I LIKE THAT ABOUT IT.

WELL, MARCE...

...THAT'S SOMETHING YOU'LL HAVE TO DECIDE FOR YOURSELF.

TO BE CONCLUDED NEXT CHAPTER!

COMMUNICATION ISSUES

story and art
POLLY GUO

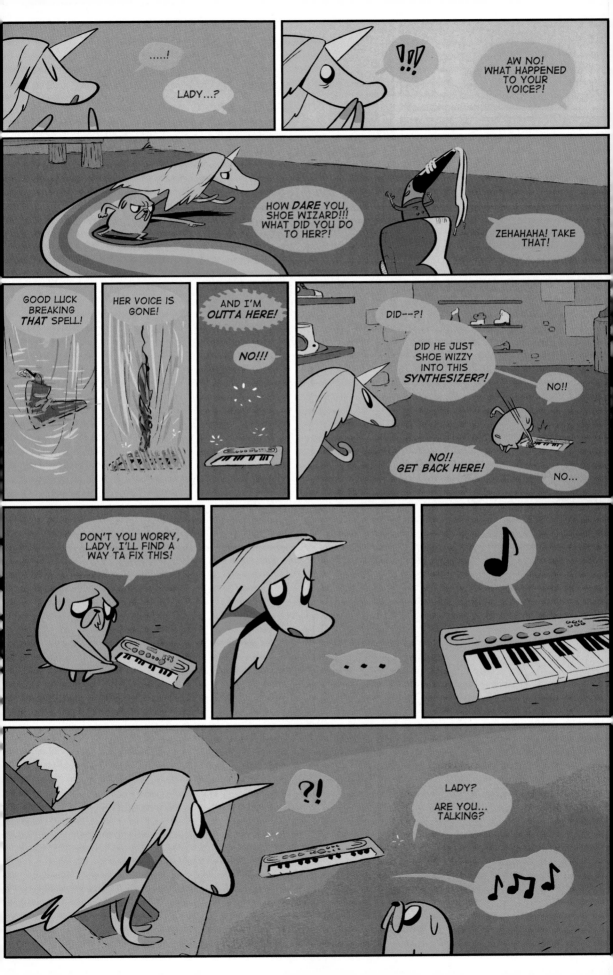

END

LOOK, IT'S TOUGH FOR ME, TOO.

AND GUY AND BONGO.

THE WHOLE BAND'S BEEN KIND OF A BUMMER SINCE YOU AND PRINCESS BUBBLEGUM HAD YOUR LITTLE FIGHT.

IT'S NOT A "LITTLE FIGHT," OKAY, KEILA? IT'S COMPLICATED.

WELL, I CAN'T TELL YOU WHAT TO DO.

YOU JUST NEED TO MAKE A DECISION.

THAT'S STILL **KIND OF** TELLING ME WHAT TO DO.

UGH... MARCELINE!!

OKAY. OKAY.

I WON'T MOVE BACK HOME... YET.

WE'LL DO THE LAST SHOW.

OUR FAREWELL SHOW.

YOU'RE GONNA BE FINE, MARCE...

... AS LONG AS **NOT ONE THING** TRIGGERS YOUR NERVES...

YO DUDES. CHECK **THESE** OUT.

DUDE. I WANT THOSE.

YEAH! I WANT MARCELINE SOCKS TOO!

MARCELINE SOCKS!

MARCELINE SOCKS!

MARCELINE SOCKS!

MARCELINE SOCKS!

MARCELINE SOCKS **BIG TIME!**

YOU'RE GONNA BE MY BREAKFAST, BABYYY...

YOU'RE GONNA BE MY **BRUNCH**!

SIGH.

LOOK, PRINCESS-- THE FINAL CONCERT!

ARE YOU **SURE** YOU DON'T WANT TO GO?

IT WOULD DO NO GOOD, TREE TRUNKS... MARCELINE WANTS IT THIS WAY.

But what about SCIENCE?!

NOT EVERYTHING CAN BE FIXED WITH SCIENCE, BMO.

WELL, I MEAN...

...MARCELINE ISN'T **JUST** BEING A JERK. SHE'S COMPOSED OF BOTH MONSTER AND HUMANOID ELEMENTS.

BUT SHE'S BEING OVERWHELMED BY ANXIETY...CAUSING AN IMBALANCE IN HER MONSTER BRAIN.

IT CAN'T BE NEUTRALIZED WITH LOGIC. THAT ONLY SENDS HER FARTHER INTO A CHAOTIC STATE.

HENCE THOSE GLOWING EYES, SHE--

GLOWING EYES, PRINCESS?

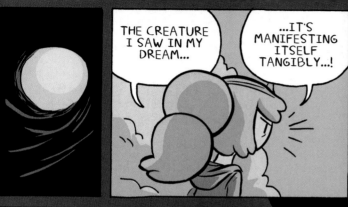

THE CREATURE I SAW IN MY DREAM...

...IT'S MANIFESTING ITSELF TANGIBLY...!

IT'S GOING TO CONSUME HER!

YOU... YOU DID THIS TO ME...!

MARCE, NO!

EW.

I DON'T KNOW WHERE THIS IS COMING FROM! WE LOVE YOU!

Y-YEAH GIRL! I DIG THE **FIERCE** LOOK!

I'LL HANDLE THIS...

STOMP

YOU AND I HAVE CREATIVE DIFFERENCES!

WE'RE YOUR FRIENDS... LET US HELP YOU...!

I HAVE NO FRIENDS!

BUBBLEGUM...!

I KNEW THERE'D BE A MESS AS SOON AS I LEFT!

ZORP

OOF!

THEY LIKE US!

UM, **MOVE!** 'SCUSE ME! YEAH, YOU! YOU TAKE UP MORE SPACE THAN YOU THINK!

OH MY **GLOB** MARCELINE! CAN YOU COMMENT ON THIS SHOW FOR A MUSIC JOURNAL?

WAIT A SECOND!

JUST NEED YOU TO SIGN THIS RELEASE FORM...

YOU'VE BEEN WRITING THAT DRIVEL?!

AAAHH! LEMME GOOO!

MUSIC JOURNALIST INDEED!

YOU NEARLY **RUINED** THE SCREAM QUEENS WITH YOUR HATEFUL VENDETTA!

N-NO WAY! I **LOVE** THE SCREAM QUEENS! THEY'RE MY FAVORITE LUMPIN' BAND OF ALL **TIME!**

THE ONLY REASON I **TOOK** THIS JOB WAS FOR ALL THE FREE MARCELINE SWAG!

THEN WHY COULDN'T YOU WRITE A **POSITIVE** REVIEW?

UM... BECAUSE THAT'S NOT HOW YOU **LIKE** SOMETHING.

YOU LIKE SOMETHING BY TELLING EVERYONE YOU **HATE** IT.

BUT... I NEVER THOUGHT I'D HURT ANYBODY!

I'LL NEVER WRITE ANYTHING NEGATIVE **AGAIN!**

YEAH, CRITICISM CAN BE HURTFUL, BUT...

MAYBE IT'S SOMETHING MY EGO NEEDS NOW AND THEN.

SO I CAN TAKE IT WITHOUT LETTING IT **CONTROL** ME.

NO, WAIT.

THAT ISN'T THE ANSWER.

OH THANK GLOB.

Y'KNOW... JUST LET IT **NAG** ME A LITTLE!

AWWWK!!